Puffi

MY DAD'S

My Dad's a Fire-Eater began life as a short, jokey poem that ran out of breath after eight lines and was laid aside.

Then in the spring of 1990, after a writing workshop at the Westminster Children's Hospital, the teachers gave me a copy of *Brave Heart* by Joanna Gillespie, a true and moving account of a little girl's battle against cancer.

In August I was visiting hospital again. This time, St Mary's, Paddington, where my wife gave birth to Isabel Mary, my first daughter. The poem suddenly returned to life, and during the hot days and nights of the late summer, I watched as it took on a new energy and sense of direction.

As the poem had been given to me by all the people referred to above, this book is for them. And for you.

Roger McGough, 1992

By the same author

THE GREAT SMILE ROBBERY
THE STOWAWAYS
SKY IN THE PIE
NAILING THE SHADOW
AN IMAGINARY MENAGERIE
HELEN HIGHWATER
PILLOW TALK
YOU TELL ME (with Michael Rosen)

(*For older readers*)
STRICTLY PRIVATE
YOU AT THE BACK

ROGER McGOUGH

My Dad's a FIRE-EATER

Illustrated by Anthony Lewis

PUFFIN BOOKS

PUFFIN BOOKS

Published by the Penguin Group
Penguin Books Ltd, 27 Wrights Lane, London W8 5TZ, England
Penguin Books USA Inc., 375 Hudson Street, New York, New York 10014, USA
Penguin Books Australia Ltd, Ringwood, Victoria, Australia
Penguin Books Canada Ltd, 10 Alcorn Avenue, Toronto, Ontario, Canada M4V 3B2
Penguin Books (NZ) Ltd, 182-190 Wairau Road, Auckland 10, New Zealand

Penguin Books Ltd, Registered Offices: Harmondsworth, Middlesex, England

Published in Puffin Books 1992
1 3 5 7 9 10 8 6 4 2

Set in 16/22pt Monotype Bembo
Colour reproduction by Anglia Graphics Ltd, Bedford
Printed in Great Britain by William Clowes Ltd, Beccles

My dad's a fire-eater
Who can do magic and juggle as well
But it's fire-eating that he's famous for
As folk round here will tell

November the Fifth began quietly
(The odd banger here and there)
With everyone looking forward
To the big display in the square

At six o'clock sharp, the bonfire was lit
And to a chorus of 'oohs' and 'aahs'
The first rocket tore into the sky
Scattering the curious stars

SPACE INFERNOS

ICE VOLCANOES

STRATOTHRUSTERS

SONIC ZAPS

PLANET BLASTERS

SLIME TORPEDOES

ATOM SPLITTERS

THUNDERCLAPS

SPIRAL SPLINTERS

MARTIAN LIGHTNING

It was going like a dream

NUCLEAR FOUNTAINS

MUTANT LOBSTERS

When suddenly, a scream!

‘The Town Hall! The Town Hall!
The roof has caught alight’
The crowd all turned as one, and felt
A shiver run through the night

A random spark? The stars' revenge?
There wasn't time to ask
The fire brigade was sent for
And set about its task

The hose unfurled, it sprung to life
Like a water-spouting snake
With a thirst to drain a reservoir
Or medium-sized lake

Snakes and ladders, ladders and snakes
The fireman's favourite games
As the ladder slowly inched its way
Toward the angry flames

The crowd cheered on its heroes
As they scrambled up the rungs
While below (and ignored) the bonfire
Grew sullen and pulled tongues

★ ★ ★

Dad missed all the excitement
He was driving home for his tea
After a matinée performance
Before coming on to see me

You'd assume that he'd be heading
Straight for the Town Hall Square
To join Mum and me for the fireworks
But he knew we wouldn't be there

Because I'm in hospital (St Mary's)
I've been here for months on end
(Leukaemia it is, not very nice
Though they say I'm on the mend)

Mum is with me night and day
In fact, she sleeps on the ward
And Dad pops along between concerts
So there's never time to be bored

Well, this particular evening
Had us jumping up and down
All excited, in front of the window
That overlooks the town

There were fairy cakes and lemonade
And the nurses made such a fuss
You'd think the pyrotechnics
Had been put on just for us

But when, of course, we saw the flames
And heard the sirens wail
It was like a needle going in
Even Matron turned quite pale

Then suddenly, an alarm bell rang
And from the corridor, a shout
The lights flickered on and off
As panic slithered out

With people rushing up and down
'Clear the wards,' they cried
'A fire's broken out in Casualty
Everyone, quickly outside'

First the Town Hall, then the hospital
Could there be an evil link?
(Both unconnected, as it happens)
But at the time it made us think

But not for long, for Matron
Took immediate command
And led us out of the building
Crocodile-fashion, hand in hand

Some on crutches, some in chairs
The bandaged and the patched
And some poor kids with catheters
And drips and things attached

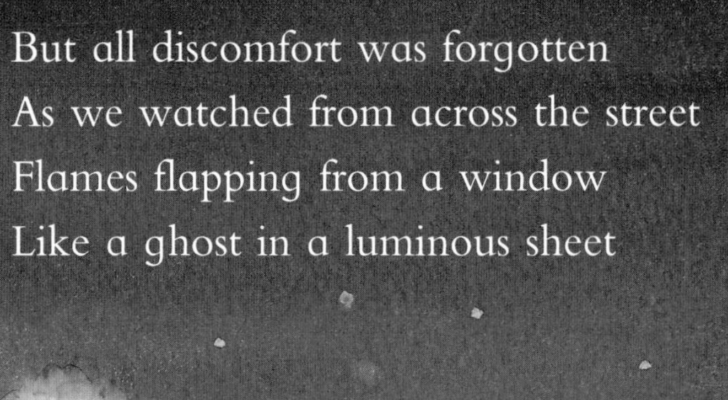

But all discomfort was forgotten
As we watched from across the street
Flames flapping from a window
Like a ghost in a luminous sheet

From one of the labs an explosion
And the sound of breaking glass
And a dragon's breath of purple smoke
And the sulphury smell of gas

Then we overheard two doctors
Say the local fire brigade
Were so tied up in town
They were bound to be delayed

But Milldyke had answered the call
And promised to save the day
(But Milldyke was in the next valley
Twenty-odd miles away!)

Meanwhile the fire, as if knowing this
And eager to end the battle
Had taken the chimney by the throat
And made its brickwork rattle

'Oh, Lor!' cried Matron, to my mum
The worries of the world upon her
'Unless a miracle is on its way
St Mary's is a goner!'

★ ★ ★

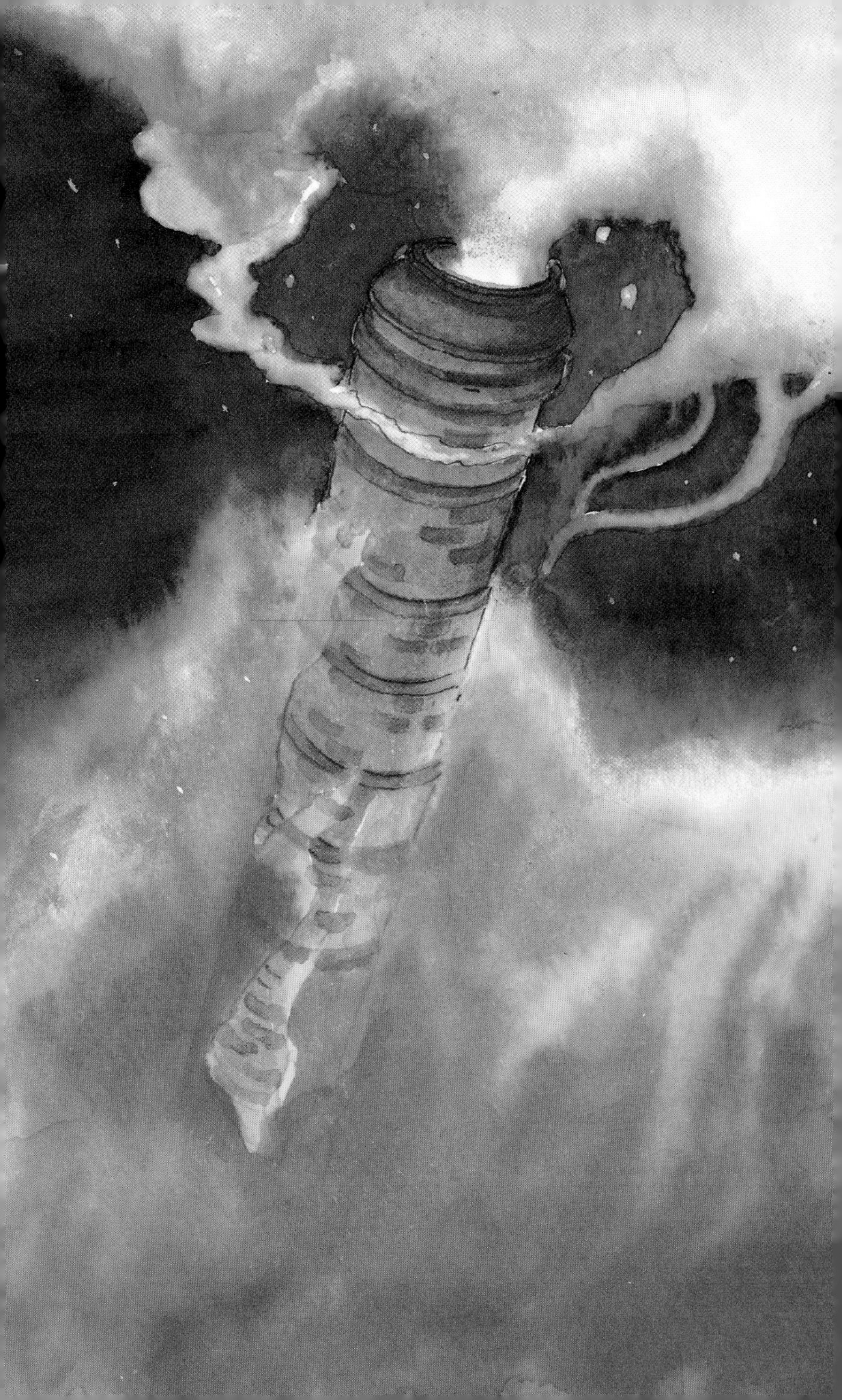

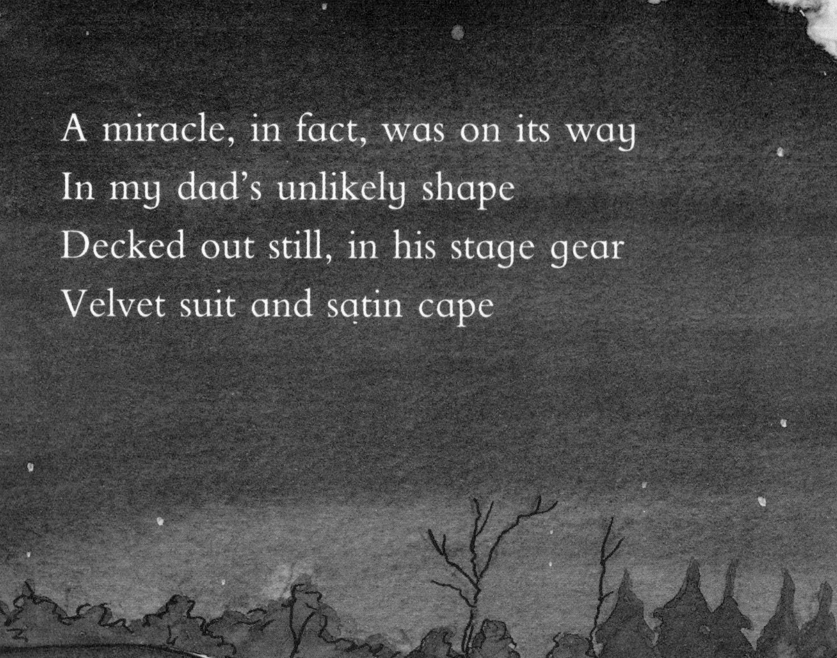

A miracle, in fact, was on its way
In my dad's unlikely shape
Decked out still, in his stage gear
Velvet suit and satin cape

I suppose it's part of his training
To enter dead on cue
And he did. Parked, took one look
And knew just what to do

Now I've seen fire-eaters many times
And it's the magic that I admire
Because I know for a fact that fire-eaters
Actually never eat - fire

Except one
My dad
That night

It was the chance he'd been waiting for
As if his whole career
Had been leading to this moment
Of death or glory here

His face took on the heroic look
He'd been rehearsing all his days
He wrapped his cloak around him
And leapt into the blaze

'God bless us and save us,' screamed Matron
'Your man will be burnt to a crisp!'
'Not wearing athbethtoth underpanth'
Joked Mum with her gentle lisp

He headed straight for the chimney
Went on all fours round its base
And like a hoover sucked the flames
Which vanished without trace

He ate the fire in the basement
Gobbled the flames in the hall
Munched the cinders that fell from the winders
And swallowed them, glass bits and all

Suddenly he ran from the inferno
Blue-faced as if to choke
'Pardon me,' he gasped politely
And burped a cloud of smoke

Then he blew a kiss to the nurses
(He was always one for the ladies)
Before plunging once again
Into the furnace of Hades

And he chewed the fire, consumed the fire
Swallowed the fire, until
Not a single spark remained
As the fire engines came over the hill

His costume in tatters, his face black as soot
So weary, he hardly could stand
But not too tired to raise a smile
Kiss Mum and squeeze my hand

Flabbergasted were the firemen
Just couldn't believe their ears
They looked at my dad in amazement
Then gave three hearty cheers

Took off their helmets

Raised their arms

And gave three hearty cheers

★ ★ ★

St Mary's was saved, and in time
It was back to things as they were
Though my hair has started to grow now
And I seem to have energy to spare

And Matron says that, fingers crossed
If results turn out as they should
They'll let me go home in a fortnight
And I'm not coming back, touch wood

And when I grow up I'm going to be
A fire-eater just like my dad
If not, it doesn't matter
Life's too short to be sad.